IGOR STRAVINSKY

CONCERTO EN RÉ

for Violin

Ernst Eulenburg Ltd

London · Mainz · Madrid · New York · Paris · Prague · Tokyo · Toronto · Zürich

CONTENTS / INHALT

PREFACE / VORWORT

When Stravinsky made the decision, at the beginning of 1931, to write a concerto for violin and orchestra, he was faced with the same problem as Johannes Brahms before him and Béla Bartók after him: '[...] I am not a violinist and I was afraid that my slight knowledge of that instrument would not be sufficient to enable me to solve the many problems that would necessarily arise in the course of a major work specially composed for it.'[1] Just as Brahms worked extremely closely with the violinist Joseph Joachim when completing his violin concerto, and Bartók with Zoltán Székely, so it can be said that without the collaboration of Samuel Dushkin the Stravinsky Concerto in its existing form would have been inconceivable. The composer admittedly added a qualification: 'I was not a complete novice when it came to handling the Violin Concerto. In my pieces for string quartet,[2] in many passages in the score of *Pulcinella*,[3] but most of all in *The Soldier's Tale*[4] I had had occasion to use the violin as a solo instrument and to become familiar with its technique.'[5] A degree of uncertainty on Stravinsky's part, however, cannot be overlooked, especially since he also sought advice from Paul Hindemith, one of the best violin and viola players of the time: 'I asked him whether the fact that I did not

Als Strawinsky Anfang 1931 den Entschluß faßte, ein Konzert für Violine und Orchester zu schreiben, sah er sich demselben Problem gegenüber wie vor ihm Johannes Brahms und nach ihm Béla Bartók: „Da ich selber kein Geiger bin, fürchtete ich, daß die summarische Kenntnis, die ich von diesem Instrument habe, nicht genügen werde, um die vielfachen Probleme zu lösen, die sich mit Notwendigkeit ergeben, wenn man ein größeres Werk für Violine komponiert."[1] Arbeitete Brahms bei der Fertigstellung seines Violinkonzerts aufs engste mit dem Geiger Joseph Joachim und Bartók mit Zoltán Székely zusammen, so kann man davon ausgehen, daß ohne die Mitwirkung Samuel Dushkins das Strawinsky-Konzert in der vorliegenden Gestalt undenkbar wäre. Zwar schränkte der Komponist ein: „Ich war in der Behandlung des Violinkonzerts kein völliger Neuling. In meinen Stücken für Streichquartett[2] und in zahlreichen Stellen der Partitur zu *Pulcinella*[3], aber vor allem in der *Geschichte vom Soldaten*[4] hatte ich Gelegenheit gehabt, die Geige als Soloinstrument zu verwenden und mir ihre Technik anzueignen."[5] Eine gewisse Unsicherheit jedoch war nicht zu übersehen, zumal sich Strawinsky noch von Paul Hindemith, einem der besten Geiger und Brat-

---

[1] Igor Stravinsky, *Chroniques de ma vie*, Paris 1935/36; Engl. trans. London 1936, quoted in Eric Walter White, *Stravinsky: The Composer and His Works*, London 1966, pp. 78-9

[2] The Three Pieces for String Quartet (1914) and the Concertino for String Quartet (1920)

[3] cf. especially the passages for concertante string quartet

[4] cf. Rudolf Stephan, 'Die Violinmusik des zwanzigsten Jahrhunderts', in *Violinspiel und Violinmusik in Geschichte und Gegenwart*, ed. Vera Schwartz, Vienna 1975, pp. 60-79 (66-9)

[5] Stravinsky, *Chroniques*, op. cit.

[1] Igor Strawinsky, *Mein Leben*, München 1956, S. 152

[2] die *Drei Stück für Streichquartett* (1914) und das *Concertino* für Streichquartett (1920)

[3] vgl. darin vor allem die Abschnitte des konzertierenden Streichquartetts

[4] vgl. Rudolf Stephan, *Die Violinmusik des Zwanzigsten Jahrhunderts*, in: *Violinspiel und Violinmusik in Geschichte und Gegenwart* (hg. von Vera Schwarz), Wien 1975, S. 60 - 79 (66 - 69)

[5] Strawinsky, a.a.O., S. 154

play the violin would not inevitably be to the disadvantage of my composition. He reassured me completely by saying that, on the contrary, he thought it would help me to avoid a routine technique and would give rise to ideas that would not be suggested by the familiar movement of the fingers.'[6]

The Polish-American violinist Samuel Dushkin, adopted son of the American composer Blair Fairchild, had studied under Leopold Auer in New York and Fritz Kreisler in Paris and had already done twelve years of concert work before he met Stravinsky. The meeting took place at the beginning of 1931 in the Wiesbaden home of Willy Strecker, through Strecker's influence and that of his brother Ludwig, head of the music publishers B. Schott's Söhne of Mainz. Stravinsky recalled: 'From my first meeting with Dushkin I could tell that he was just as Willy Strecker had described. Before I got to know him I had been somewhat mistrustful, despite the importance I was bound to attach to the recommendation of a refined and cultivated friend. I was afraid of finding in Dushkin the characteristic features of the virtuoso. [...] Dushkin is an unusual exception within his profession. I was very happy to find that, besides his remarkable gifts as a born violinist, he possessed musical culture, a delicate understanding and – in the exercise of his profession – an abnegation that is very rare.'[7]

The violinist, then on the brink of forty, matched Stravinsky's strict criteria of selection: 'negative' criteria, in the sense that Stravinsky's account indicates not so much that his wishes were fulfilled as that his fears were *not* fulfilled. This attitude tallied with

schisten seiner Zeit, darüber beraten ließ: „Ich fragte ihn, ob die Tatsache, daß ich nicht Geige spiele, meiner Komposition nicht zum Nachteil gereichen müsse. Er beruhigte mich völlig, denn er meinte, daß ganz im Gegenteil diese Tatsache mir helfen würde, jede technische Routine zu vermeiden, und so hätte ich es viel leichter, eine Musik zu schreiben, die nicht von den gewohnten Fingerbewegungen beeinflußt sei."[6]

Der polnisch-amerikanische Geiger Samuel Dushkin, Adoptivsohn des amerikanischen Komponisten Blair Fairchild, hatte in New York bei Leopold Auer und in Paris bei Fritz Kreisler studiert und bereits zwölf Jahre Konzertpraxis absolviert, bevor er auf Vermittlung von Willy Strecker, gemeinsam mit seinem Bruder Ludwig Verlagsleiter des Musikverlags B. Schott's Söhne, Mainz, Anfang 1931 in dessen Wiesbadener Wohnung mit Strawinsky zusammenkam. Dieser erinnerte sich: „Schon bei meinem ersten Zusammentreffen mit Dushkin konnte ich feststellen, daß er genau so war, wie ihn Willy Strecker geschildert hatte. Bevor ich ihn kannte, war ich etwas mißtrauisch gewesen, trotz der Bedeutung, die ich einer Empfehlung durch meinen feinen und kultivierten Freund beimessen mußte. Ich fürchtete, bei Dushkin die Eigenschaften des Virtuosen zu finden [...] Dushkin ist unter seinen Berufsgenossen eine seltene Ausnahme. Ich war sehr glücklich, bei ihm außer den bedeutenden Gaben des geborenen Geigers auch eine hohe musikalische Kultur zu finden, ein feines Verständnis und eine wirklich ungewöhnliche Zurückhaltung bei der Ausübung seines Berufs."[7]

Der damals knapp vierzigjährige Geiger entsprach der strengen Auslese Strawinskys, einer „negativen" Auslese, insofern sich in seiner Beschreibung weniger Wunscherfüllung als die Nichterfüllung von Befürchtungen ausdrückt – ein Ge-

---

[6] Ibid.
[7] Ibid.

[6] a.a.O., S. 155
[7] a.a.O., S. 153

V

Stravinsky's account of the creative process: 'All art presupposes a work of selection. Usually when I set to work my goal is not definite. If I were asked what I wanted at this stage of the creative process, I should be hard pressed to say. But I should always give an exact answer when asked what I did *not* want.'[8]

Dushkin, for his part, later described his experience of collaborating with Stravinsky: 'During the winter [of 1930–31] I saw Stravinsky in Paris quite often. One day when we were lunching in a restaurant, Stravinsky took out a piece of paper and wrote down this chord:

and asked me if it could be played. I had never seen a chord with such an enormous stretch, from the E to the top A, and I said "No". Stravinsky said sadly "Quel dommage" (what a pity). After I got home, I tried it, and, to my astonishment, I found that in that register, the stretch of the eleventh was relatively easy to play, and the sound fascinated me. I telephoned Stravinsky at once to tell him that it could be done. When the Concerto was finished, more than six months later, I understood his disappointment when I first said "No". This chord, in a different dress, begins each of the four movements. Stravinsky himself calls it his "passport" to that Concerto.'[9] The chord, incidentally, involves a 'constellation of fifths': three notes (here, D, A and E) standing at the interval of a fifth to one

sichtspunkt, der auch dem Schaffensprozeß entsprach: „Jede Kunst setzt eine auswählende Tätigkeit voraus. Wenn ich an die Arbeit gehe, habe ich meist kein klares Ziel vor Augen. Würde man mich in diesem Stadium meiner Operation fragen, was ich will, so hätte ich Mühe, es zu sagen; aber ich würde jederzeit präzis antworten, wenn man mich fragte, was ich nicht will."[8]

Auch Dushkin hat über seine Erfahrungen in der Zusammenarbeit mit Strawinsky berichtet: „Über Winter [1930/31] sah ich Strawinsky in Paris ziemlich oft. Als wir eines Tages in einem Restaurant zu Mittag aßen, zog er ein Stück Papier heraus, schrieb den Akkord

hin und fragte mich, ob er spielbar sei. Ich hatte niemals einen Akkord von so enormer Spannweite von E bis zum hohen A gesehen und sagte: ,Nein.' Strawinsky meinte traurig: ,Quel dommage' (Wie schade). Als ich wieder zu Hause war, versuchte ich den Akkord und fand zu meinem Erstaunen, daß die Undezim-Spannung in dieser Lage verhältnismäßig leicht ausführbar war, und der Klang faszinierte mich. Ich rief Strawinsky sogleich an, um ihm zu sagen, daß der Akkord gespielt werden könne. Als das Konzert mehr als sechs Monate später beendet war, verstand ich seine Enttäuschung darüber, daß ich zuerst Nein gesagt hatte. Dieser Akkord beginnt in verschiedener Einkleidung jeden der vier Sätze. Strawinsky selbst nennt ihn den ,Paß' zu diesem Konzert."[9] Es handelt sich

[8] Igor Stravinsky, *Poetics of Music,* transl. Arthur Knodel and Ingolf Dahl, Cambridge, Mass. 1942, 1970, p. 89
[9] Samuel Dushkin, 'Working with Stravinsky', in *Stravinsky,* ed. Edwin Corle, New York 1949; quoted in White, op. cit., p. 330

[8] Igor Strawinsky, *Musikalische Poetik,* in: ders., *Schriften und Gespräche I,* Mainz 1983, S. 214
[9] Samuel Dushkin, *Arbeit und Zusammenarbeit,* in: *Musik der Zeit* (hg. von Heinrich Lindlar und Reinhold Schubert), Neue Folge, Heft 1 (*Strawinsky, Wirklichkeit und Wirkung*), Bonn 1958, S. 81 – 86 (aus: Samuel Dushkin, *Working with Stravinsky,* New York 1949). Notenbeispiel in der deutschen Fassung nicht enthalten.

another (with octave displacement). This is one of Stravinsky's favoured cadential devices.[10]

Increasingly it became Dushkin's task to bring Stravinsky's compositional ideas into harmony with the concertante requirements of the violin. At varying intervals Stravinsky would show him what he had just written, perhaps a page, perhaps only a few lines, perhaps half a movement. They then discussed all the suggestions that Dushkin came up with. 'Whenever he accepted one of my suggestions, even a simple change such as extending the range of the violin by stretching the phrase to the octave below and the octave above, Stravinsky would insist on altering the very foundations correspondingly. He behaved like an architect who if asked to change a room on the third floor had to go down to the foundations to keep the proportions of the whole structure.'[11]

Stravinsky gives unusually precise scoring instructions for his Violin Concerto, especially as regards the strings (the strength of the double basses is striking): piccolo, 2 flutes, 2 oboes, cor anglais, E flat clarinet, 2 clarinets, 3 bassoons (3rd also double bassoon), 4 horns, 3 trumpets, 3 trombones (3rd also bass trombone), tuba; timpani; 8 first violins, 8 second violins, 6 violas, 4 cellos, 6 double basses. The first two movements and part of the third were composed in Nice in the spring of 1931; the work was completed at La Vironnière, a country estate near Voreppe (Val d'Isère), where Stravinsky spent the sum-

bei diesem Akkord übrigens um einen „Quintkörper": um Töne, die – hier D, A, E – oktavversetzt jeweils im Quintabstand zueinander stehen - ein bei Strawinsky stets beliebtes Kadenzierungsmittel[10].

Dushkins Aufgabe wurde es mit der Zeit immer mehr, Strawinskys kompositorische Vorstellungen mit den konzertanten Ansprüchen der Geige in Einklang zu bringen. „In verschiedenen Zeitabständen pflegte er mir zu zeigen, was er gerade geschrieben hatte, manchmal eine Seite, manchmal nur wenige Zeilen, machmal einen halben Satz. Dann sprachen wir alle Anregungen durch, die ich geben konnte. So oft er einen meiner Vorschläge annahm – auch wenn es sich nur um eine einfache Veränderung wie die Erweiterung des Klangbereichs der Violine durch Ausdehnung der Phrase in die untere oder obere Oktave handelte –, bestand Strawinsky in der Regel darauf, die gesamten Grundlagen zu ändern. Er handelte dabei wie ein Architekt, der beim Fundament beginnen mußte, um die Proportionen des ganzen Baues zu erhalten, wenn von ihm verlangt wurde, einen Raum im dritten Stock zu verändern."[11]

Für die Orchesterbesetzung seines Violinkonzerts hat Strawinsky vor allem im Bereich der Streicher ungewöhnlich präzise Angaben gemacht (auffallend die stark besetzten Kontrabässe): Piccoloflöte, 2 Flöten, 2 Oboen, Englischhorn, Es-Klarinette, 2 Klarinetten, 3 Fagotte (3. auch Kontrafagott), 4 Hörner, 3 Trompeten, 3 Posaunen (3. auch Baßposaune), Tuba; Pauken; 8 erste und 8 zweite Violinen, 6 Bratschen, 4 Violoncelli, 6 Kontrabässe. Komponiert wurden die ersten beiden und ein Teil des dritten Satzes im Frühjahr 1931 in Nizza; abgeschlossen wurde das Werk auf La Vironnière, einem Landsitz bei Voreppe

---

[10] cf. *Oedipus Rex* (e.g. the chords heavily saturated with fifths in the trumpet fanfares, rehearsal nos. 170–72)
[11] Dushkin, in White, op. cit., p. 330

[10] vgl. *Oedipus Rex* (z. B. die stark quintgesättigten Akkorde in den Trompetenfanfaren Z. 170–172)
[11] Dushkin, a.a.O., S. 83

mer. The first performance took place on 23 October 1931 in Berlin, with Samuel Dushkin as soloist and Stravinsky conducting. The manuscript has no dedication, but contains a note signed by the composer: 'Cette œuvre a été créée sous ma direction le 23 octobre 1931 au concert du Rundfunk de Berlin par Samuel Dushkin auquel je garde une reconnaissance profonde et une grande admiration pour la valeur hautement artistique de son jeu.' A few weeks before the first performance the composer prepared a reduction for violin and piano (with the concluding note 'Voreppe le 4 Sept. 1931').

In his conversations with his assistant Robert Craft published in 1961[12], Stravinsky emphasized that the Violin Concerto did not follow any model: 'I did not find that the standard violin concertos – Mozart's, Beethoven's, or even Brahms's – were among their composers' best work. (The Schoenberg concerto is an exception, but that is hardly standard yet.) The subtitles of my Concerto – *Toccata, Aria, Capriccio* – may suggest Bach, and so, in a superficial way, might the musical substance. I am very fond of the Bach Concerto for Two Violins, as the duet of the soloist with a violin from the orchestra in the last movement of my own Concerto may show. But my Concerto employs other duet combinations too, and the texture is almost always more characteristic of chamber music than of orchestral music.

I did not compose a cadenza, not because I did not care about exploiting the violin virtuosity, but because the violin in combination was my real interest. But vir-

(Val d'Isère), wo Strawinsky den Sommer verbrachte. Die Uraufführung fand am 23. Oktober 1931 in Berlin mit Samuel Dushkin als Solisten und Strawinsky als Dirigenten statt. Das Manuskript ist ohne Widmung, enthält jedoch eine vom Komponisten unterzeichnete Notiz: „Cette œuvre a été créée sous ma direction le 23 octobre 1931 au concert du Rundfunk de Berlin par Samuel Dushkin auquel je garde une reconnaissance profonde et une grande admiration pour la valeur hautement artistique de son jeu." Wenige Wochen vor der Uraufführung fertigte der Komponist (mit Abschlußvermerk „Voreppe le 4 Sept. 1931") einen Auszug für Violine und Klavier an.

In seinen 1961 veröffentlichten Gesprächen mit seinem Assistenten Robert Craft[12] legte Strawinsky Wert auf die Feststellung, daß das Violinkonzert keinem Modell folge. „Ich fand nicht, daß die Standard-Violinkonzerte – von Mozart, Beethoven oder selbst Brahms – zum Besten dieser Komponisten zählte. (Das Schönberg-Konzert bildet eine Ausnahme, obwohl es weit davon entfernt ist, zum Standardrepertoire gezählt zu werden.) Die Untertitel meines Konzerts – *Toccata, Aria, Capriccio* – mögen einen Einfluß Bachs nahelegen, ebenso, wenn auch nur oberflächlich, die musikalische Substanz. Ich schätze Bachs Doppelkonzert für zwei Violinen, wie es im letzten Satz das Duo zwischen dem Solisten und einem der Geiger andeuten mag. Doch verwendet mein Konzert auch andere Duo-Kombinationen, und überhaupt ähnelt seine Beschaffenheit eher einer kammermusikalischen als einer Orchesterkomposition.

Ich habe auf eine Kadenz verzichtet, nicht, weil mich der Nutzen geigerischer Virtuosität nicht interessierte, sondern weil mein Anliegen die Kombinationsmöglich-

---

[12] Igor Stravinsky and Robert Craft, *Dialogues*, Berkeley/Los Angeles 1982, pp. 47ff.

[12] Igor Strawinsky/Robert Craft, *Dialogues*, Berkeley/Los Angeles 1982, S. 47 f.

tuosity for its own sake has only a small role in my Concerto, and the technical demands of the piece are relatively tame.'

Manfred Karallus
Translation Richard Deveson

keiten der Violine mit den Instrumenten des Orchesters betraf. Virtuosität um ihrer selbst willen spielt in meinem Konzert nur eine geringe Rolle, und die technischen Anforderungen des Stückes halte ich für relativ zahm."

Manfred Karallus

Orchestration/Orchesterbesetzung

Flauto piccolo
Flauto grande 1, 2
Oboe 1, 2
Corno inglese
Clarinetto piccolo
Clarinetto 1, 2
Fagotto 1 – 3
Corno 1 – 4
Tromba 1 – 3
Trombone 1 – 3
Tuba
Timpani
8 Violini I
8 Violini II
6 Viole
4 Violoncelli
4 Contrabassi

CONCERTO EN RÉ

Igor Stravinsky
(1882–1971)

I. Toccata

9

14

16

II. Aria I

24

68
Fl gr 1 2
Cor ingl
Cl 1 2
Fag 1 2
Trb 1 2 (basso)3
Viol Solo
cresc.
f
Viol 1 2
Viole
Vcl

30

III. Aria II

IV. Capriccio

46